CGP
— books
like no others!

GCSE English Literature AQA Anthology

Characters & Voices

The Workbook
Higher Level

This book will help you prepare for the Anthology
part of your GCSE English Literature exam.

It contains lots of questions designed to make you an
expert on writing about poetry.

It's ideal for use as a homework book or to help you revise.

What CGP is all about

Our sole aim here at CGP is to produce the highest quality
books — carefully written, immaculately presented and
dangerously close to being funny.

Then we work our socks off to get them out to you
— at the cheapest possible prices.

CONTENTS

Section Three — Themes

Section Four — Analysing Answers

Published by Coordination Group Publications Ltd.

Editors:
Heather Gregson, Edward Robinson, Hayley Thompson

Produced with:
Alison Smith, Peter Thomas, Nicola Woodfin

Contributors:
Karen Fallows, Alison Smith

With thanks to Glenn Rogers and Robert Teed for the proofreading
and Jan Greenway for copyright research.

ISBN: 978 1 84762 522 9
Groovy website: www.cgpbooks.co.uk
Jolly bits of clipart from CorelDRAW®
Printed by Elanders Hindson Ltd, Newcastle upon Tyne

Based on the classic CGP style created by Richard Parsons.

How to Use this Book

This book is for anyone studying the <u>Characters and Voices</u> cluster of the AQA GCSE English Literature <u>Poetry Anthology</u>. It's got loads of <u>questions</u> in it to help you get your head around the poems.

Sections One and Two are About the Poems

There's a double page on each poem. It looks a bit like this:

There's some info about the <u>poet</u> here.

There's plenty of <u>space</u> around the poem for you to make <u>notes</u>.

Difficult words are defined in the <u>Poem Dictionary</u>.

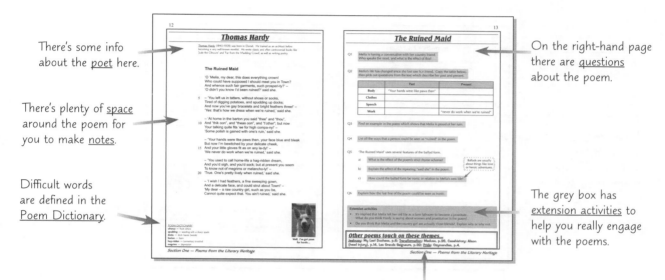

On the right-hand page there are <u>questions</u> about the poem.

The grey box has <u>extension activities</u> to help you really engage with the poems.

The top tip box lists some of the <u>other poems</u> in the cluster with <u>similar themes</u>.

A little bit about the questions...

This is the most important bit...

1) The questions are designed to get you <u>thinking for yourself</u> about the poem.
2) They start off nice and <u>simple</u>, then get <u>trickier</u> as you go down the page.
3) Answer the questions as <u>thoroughly</u> as you can.
   It's important to get to know the poems <u>inside out</u>.
4) Answers can be found in the <u>separate Answer Book</u>.

The questions in these two sections mostly ask you about <u>technical</u> stuff like <u>language</u>, <u>structure</u> and <u>form</u>.

How to Use this Book

Comparing the poems is one of the most important things you'll have to do — that's what Section Three is all about. The questions in it will help you link the different poems by their themes.

Section Three is About the Themes

A double-page spread in the Themes section looks a bit like this:

A different theme is covered on each page.

There are questions about the theme and how different poems relate to it.

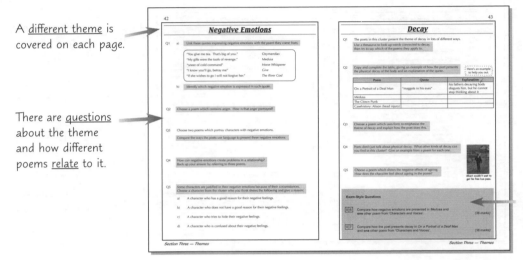

The grey box has exam-style questions relating to the themes.

This is a Really Useful Section

1) The questions are designed to get you thinking about the poems' themes and ideas.

2) They'll also get you to compare the poems — which is just what you'll need to do to get good marks in your exam.

3) The exam-style questions are exactly that — questions like the ones you'll get in your exam. Use them to practise planning and writing answers. Trust me, it'll really help when it comes to the real thing.

Remember: the themes covered in this section aren't the only ones you can write about — they're here to give you some ideas. Once you start thinking about the poems and comparing them with each other, you're bound to come up with a few more of your own.

How to Use this Book

One of the <u>best ways</u> to learn what gets you marks is to <u>analyse</u> some <u>exam-style answers</u>. So that's what you'll be doing in Section Four. You <u>lucky thing</u>, you.

Section Four lets you Analyse some Answers

A page in Section Four looks a bit like this:

There's an exam-style question at the top of the page.

This is a sample extract from a student's answer.

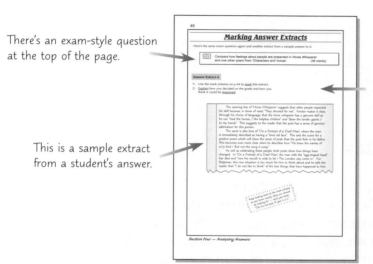

These instructions tell you what you have to do (more on this below).

This Section Helps You Understand How to Do Well

1) Most of the questions in this section ask you to <u>grade</u> a <u>sample exam answer</u>.

2) They'll also ask you to say what the answer needs to do to <u>score more marks</u> — this will help you understand how to <u>improve</u> your own answers.

3) Some of the questions ask you to <u>extend a point</u> or <u>give a quote</u> from the poem to back a point up. This helps you to understand how to really <u>use the poems</u> to write a top-notch answer.

> <u>Remember</u>: there's <u>more than one right answer</u> to the questions that you'll get in your poetry exam. These sample answers are just designed to show you the <u>kinds of points</u> you'll need to make and the <u>kind of writing style</u> you'll need to use to get a top grade.

Percy Bysshe Shelley

Percy Bysshe Shelley (1792-1822) was born in Horsham, West Sussex. He was educated at Eton and Oxford University, where he published his first novel, before being expelled in 1811. Although he is now famous for his poetry, Shelley enjoyed little literary success during his lifetime.

Ozymandias

I met a traveller from an antique land
Who said: Two vast and trunkless legs of stone
Stand in the desert. Near them on the sand,
Half sunk, a shatter'd visage lies, whose frown
5   And wrinkled lip and sneer of cold command
Tell that its sculptor well those passions read
Which yet survive, stamp'd on these lifeless things,
The hand that mock'd them and the heart that fed;
And on the pedestal these words appear:
10   'My name is Ozymandias, king of kings:
Look on my works, ye Mighty, and despair!'
Nothing beside remains. Round the decay
Of that colossal wreck, boundless and bare,
The lone and level sands stretch far away.

POEM DICTIONARY

Ozymandias — another name for Rameses II, a ruler of Ancient Egypt
antique — from a long time ago
trunkless — without a body
visage — face
pedestal — base of a statue
colossal — very large

Ozymandias

Q1   This poem is a sonnet.

   a)   What features of the poem tell you that this is a sonnet?

   b)   Is this a conventional or unconventional sonnet in terms of content and style? Explain your answer.

Q2   How does the tone of the poem change in line 12?

Q3   What is the effect of the enjambment in the poem?

Q4   In the poem, the sculptor "stamp'd" the ruler's face onto the statue. What is the effect of this image?

Q5   Explain what the contrast in this line tells you about the ruler:

   "The hand that mock'd them and the heart that fed".

Talk to the hand...

Q6   How does the poet present his ideas about the following themes:

   a)   power   b)   time   c)   pride

Extension activities

- Why do you think the poet describes the statue from a traveller's point of view?
- Find out about the English government in 1818, the year the poem was published. Could Shelley have been making some kind of political comment in this poem?

Compare the themes in this poem with...

Pride: The River God, p.8, My Last Duchess, p.6; Power: Medusa, p.26; Decay: On a Portrait of a Deaf Man, p.16, Casehistory: Alison (head injury), p.14, The Clown Punk, p.22.

Robert Browning

She rode with round the terrace – all and each
30 Would draw from her alike the approving speech,
Or blush, at least. She thanked men, – good! but thanked
Somehow – I know not how – as if she ranked
My gift of a nine-hundred-years-old name
With anybody's gift. Who'd stoop to blame
35 This sort of trifling? Even had you skill
In speech – (which I have not) – to make your will
Quite clear to such an one, and say, 'Just this
Or that in you disgusts me; here you miss,
Or there exceed the mark' – and if she let
40 Herself be lessoned so, nor plainly set
Her wits to yours, forsooth, and made excuse,
– E'en then would be some stooping; and I choose
Never to stoop. Oh sir, she smiled, no doubt,
Whene'er I passed her; but who passed without
45 Much the same smile? This grew; I gave commands;
Then all smiles stopped together. There she stands
As if alive. Will't please you rise? We'll meet
The company below, then. I repeat,
The Count your master's known munificence
50 Is ample warrant that no just pretence
Of mine for dowry will be disallowed;
Though his fair daughter's self, as I avowed
At starting, is my object. Nay, we'll go
Together down, sir. Notice Neptune, though,
55 Taming a sea-horse, thought a rarity,
Which Claus of Innsbruck cast in bronze for me!

POEM DICTIONARY
countenance — face
durst — dare
mantle — cloak
bough — branch
forsooth — indeed
officious — flattering
munificence — generosity
dowry — money paid to a man by his bride's family when they marry
avowed — said
Neptune — Roman god of the sea

Robert Browning

Robert Browning (1812-1889) was born in Camberwell, Surrey. He read and wrote poems from an early age. He married Elizabeth Barrett, another well-known poet. He produced many collections of poems, before he died in Venice, Italy.

My Last Duchess

Ferrara

That's my last Duchess painted on the wall,
Looking as if she were alive. I call
That piece a wonder, now: Frà Pandolf's hands
Worked busily a day, and there she stands.
5   Will't please you sit and look at her? I said
'Frà Pandolf' by design, for never read
Strangers like you that pictured countenance,
The depth and passion of its earnest glance,
But to myself they turned (since none puts by
10   The curtain I have drawn for you, but I)
And seemed as they would ask me, if they durst
How such a glance came there; so, not the first
Are you to turn and ask thus. Sir, 'twas not
Her husband's presence only, called that spot
15   Of joy into the Duchess' cheek: perhaps
Frà Pandolf chanced to say 'Her mantle laps
Over my lady's wrist too much,' or 'Paint
Must never hope to reproduce the faint
Half-flush that dies along her throat': such stuff
20   Was courtesy, she thought, and cause enough
For calling up that spot of joy. She had
A heart — how shall I say? — too soon made glad,
Too easily impressed; she liked whate'er
She looked on, and her looks went everywhere.
25   Sir, 'twas all one! My favour at her breast,
The dropping of the daylight in the West,
The bough of cherries some officious fool
Broke in the orchard for her, the white mule

THIS IS A FLAP.
FOLD THIS PAGE OUT.

My Last Duchess

Q1   a)   What is the effect of the iambic pentameter in the poem?

      b)   How does the poet use caesura within the poem?

Q2   Describe how the Duke felt about the Duchess's behaviour towards other men.

Q3   We learn a lot about the Duke's feelings from his monologue.
      Find an example from the poem that shows the Duke feels:

           a)   jealousy

           b)   possessiveness

           c)   power

           d)   anger

Don't make him angry

Q4   What is the significance of the portrait of the Duchess in the poem?

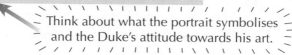

Think about what the portrait symbolises
and the Duke's attitude towards his art.

Q5   a)   Find three quotes which suggest that the Duke killed the Duchess.

      b)   What is the effect of these hints on the reader?

Q6   Explain why the statue of Neptune "Taming a sea-horse" might be an
      appropriate way to end the poem.

Extension activities

- Try and find out more about what aristocrats like the Duke were like around the time the poem
  was published in 1842. Do you think Browning liked the aristocracy?

- What kind of questions do you think the visitor might want to ask the Duke?

Other poems touch on these themes...

Power: Ozymandias, p.4; Jealousy: Medusa, p.26, The River God, p.8; Death: On a Portrait
of a Deaf Man, p.16; Relationships: Les Grands Seigneurs, p.32.

Stevie Smith

<u>Stevie Smith</u> (1902-1971), real name 'Florence', was born in Kingston upon Hull, but spent most
of her life living in North London with her aunt, working for Newnes Publishing Company.
She was awarded the Queen's Gold Medal for Poetry in 1969.

The River God

I may be smelly and I may be old,
Rough in my pebbles, reedy in my pools,
But where my fish float by I bless their swimming
And I like the people to bathe in me, especially women.
5   But I can drown the fools
Who bathe too close to the weir, contrary to rules.
And they take a long time drowning
As I throw them up now and then in the spirit of clowning.
Hi yih, yippity-yap, merrily I flow,
10 O I may be an old foul river but I have plenty of go.
Once there was a lady who was too bold
She bathed in me by the tall black cliff where the water runs cold,
So I brought her down here
To be my beautiful dear.
15 Oh will she stay with me will she stay
This beautiful lady, or will she go away?
She lies in my beautiful deep river bed with many a weed
To hold her, and many a waving reed.
Oh who would guess what a beautiful white face lies there
20 Waiting for me to smooth and wash away the fear
She looks at me with. Hi yih, do not let her
Go. There is no one on earth who does not forget her
Now. They say I am a foolish old smelly river
But they do not know of my wide original bed
25 Where the lady waits, with her golden sleepy head.
If she wishes to go I will not forgive her.

Ooh, I'm so scared...

<u>POEM DICTIONARY</u>
weir — dam built across a river

Section One — Poems from the Literary Heritage

The River God

Q1 From line 5, the poem uses rhyming couplets. Copy this table, then write down examples of rhyming couplets and explain the significance of each pair of words.

Couplet	Effect
"drowning" / "clowning"	

We've put one here to start you off.

Q2 Explain the effect of the childlike language such as "yippity-yap" in the poem.

Q3 Why does the River God repeat that he is "old" and "smelly"?

Q4 Look at this extract from the poem:

"Go. There is no one on earth who does not forget her
Now. They say I am a foolish old smelly river"

What is the effect of the highlighted words?

Q5 The final line is ambiguous. Give as many interpretations for this line as you can.

Extension activities

• What kind of cultures or religions might believe in river gods? Could the poem be about changing religious beliefs?

• What do you think the poet is saying about nature in the poem?

Several poems have similar themes...

Death: My Last Duchess, p.6, Medusa, p.26, On a Portrait of a Deaf Man, p.16; Power: Ozymandias, p.4; Decay: The Clown Punk, p.22, Casehistory: Alison (head injury), p.14.

Dylan Thomas

Dylan Thomas (1914-1953) was born and raised in Swansea. He left school at 16 and his first job was as a newspaper reporter. As well as poetry, Thomas wrote prose and drama, including the play 'Under Milk Wood'.

The Hunchback in the Park

The hunchback in the park
A solitary mister
Propped between trees and water
From the opening of the garden lock
5   That lets the trees and water enter
Until the Sunday sombre bell at dark

Eating bread from a newspaper
Drinking water from the chained cup
That the children filled with gravel
10   In the fountain basin where I sailed my ship
Slept at night in a dog kennel
But nobody chained him up.

Like the park birds he came early
Like the water he sat down
15   And Mister they called Hey mister
The truant boys from the town
Running when he had heard them clearly
On out of sound

Past lake and rockery
20   Laughing when he shook his paper
Hunchbacked in mockery
Through the loud zoo of the willow groves
Dodging the park keeper
With his stick that picked up leaves.

25   And the old dog sleeper
Alone between nurses and swans
While the boys among willows
Made the tigers jump out of their eyes
To roar on the rockery stones
30   And the groves were blue with sailors

Made all day until bell time
A woman figure without fault
Straight as a young elm
Straight and tall from his crooked bones
35   That she might stand in the night
After the locks and chains

All night in the unmade park
After the railings and shrubberies
The birds the grass the trees the lake
40   And the wild boys innocent as strawberries
Had followed the hunchback
To his kennel in the dark.

Is it a tree...or is it a woman?

The Hunchback in the Park

Q1 Pick out descriptions from the poem about the following characters:

　　a)　　the hunchback

　　b)　　the group of boys

　　c)　　the narrator

Q2 The poem is structured like a series of memories and observations from the narrator's past. What is the effect of this?

Q3 The boys are described as "wild boys innocent as strawberries". What could this mean?

Imagery is any language that creates a picture in your mind, including similes and metaphors.

Q4 Find three other pieces of imagery from the poem.

　　a)　　Explain the effect of each image.

　　b)　　Which image do you think is the most effective? Why?

Q5 Why do you think the hunchback is compared to nature in the poem?

Q6 Why do you think the group of boys follow the hunchback out of the park at the end?

Extension activity

• The narrator doesn't offer any direct judgement about the hunchback. Do you think he approves of the hunchback's lifestyle? Try to back up your answer with examples from the poem.

Compare the themes of this poem with...
Nature: The River God, p.8; Physical damage: Casehistory: Alison (head injury), p.14, On a Portrait of a Deaf Man, p.16; Isolation: Horse Whisperer, p.24, The Clown Punk, p.22.

Thomas Hardy

Thomas Hardy (1840-1928) was born in Dorset. He trained as an architect before becoming a very well-known novelist. He wrote classic and often controversial books like 'Jude the Obscure' and 'Far from the Madding Crowd', as well as writing poetry.

The Ruined Maid

'O 'Melia, my dear, this does everything crown!
Who could have supposed I should meet you in Town?
And whence such fair garments, such prosperi-ty?' —
'O didn't you know I'd been ruined?' said she.

5 — 'You left us in tatters, without shoes or socks,
Tired of digging potatoes, and spudding up docks;
And now you've gay bracelets and bright feathers three!' —
'Yes: that's how we dress when we're ruined,' said she.

— 'At home in the barton you said "thee" and "thou",
10 And "thik oon", and "theas oon", and "t'other"; but now
Your talking quite fits 'ee for high compa-ny!' —
'Some polish is gained with one's ruin,' said she.

— 'Your hands were like paws then, your face blue and bleak
But now I'm bewitched by your delicate cheek,
15 And your little gloves fit as on any la-dy!' —
'We never do work when we're ruined,' said she.

— 'You used to call home-life a hag-ridden dream,
And you'd sigh, and you'd sock; but at present you seem
To know not of megrims or melancho-ly!' —
20 'True. One's pretty lively when ruined,' said she.

— 'I wish I had feathers, a fine sweeping gown,
And a delicate face, and could strut about Town!' —
'My dear — a raw country girl, such as you be,
Cannot quite expect that. You ain't ruined,' said she.

POEM DICTIONARY
whence — from where
spudding — weeding with a sharp spade
docks — dock leaves (weeds)
barton — barn
hag-ridden — tormented, troubled
megrims — depression

Well, *I've* got paws for hands...

Section One — Poems from the Literary Heritage

The Ruined Maid

Q1   Melia is having a conversation with her country friend.
Who speaks the most, and what is the effect of this?

Q2   Melia's life has changed since she last saw her friend. Copy the table below, then pick out quotations from the text which describe her past and present.

	Past	Present
Body	"Your hands were like paws then"	
Clothes		
Speech		
Work		"never do work when we're ruined"

Q3   Find an example in the poem which shows that Melia is proud of her ruin.

Q4   List all the ways that a person could be seen as "ruined" in the poem.

Q5   'The Ruined Maid' uses several features of the ballad form.

    a)   What is the effect of the poem's strict rhyme scheme?

    b)   Explain the effect of the repeating "said she" in the poem.

Ballads are usually about things like love or heroic adventures.

    c)   How could the ballad form be ironic in relation to Melia's new life?

Q6   Explain how the last line of the poem could be seen as ironic.

Extension activities

- It's implied that Melia left her old life as a farm labourer to become a prostitute.
  What do you think Hardy is saying about women and prostitution in the poem?

- Do you think that Melia and the country girl are actually close friends? Explain why or why not.

Other poems touch on these themes...

<u>Jealousy</u>: My Last Duchess, p.6; <u>Transformation</u>: Medusa, p.26, Casehistory: Alison (head injury), p.14, Les Grands Seigneurs, p.32; <u>Pride</u>: Ozymandias, p.4.

Section One — Poems from the Literary Heritage

U A Fanthorpe

U A Fanthorpe (1929-2009) was born in Kent. She studied at Oxford University and worked as an English teacher. She started writing poetry when she left teaching to become a hospital clerk. She was made CBE for services to poetry in 2001, and awarded the Queen's Gold Medal for Poetry in 2003.

Casehistory: Alison (head injury)

(She looks at her photograph)

I would like to have known
My husband's wife, my mother's only daughter.
A bright girl she was.

Enmeshed in comforting
5 Fat, I wonder at her delicate angles.
Her autocratic knee

Like a Degas dancer's
Adjusts to the observer with airy poise,
That now lugs me upstairs

10 Hardly. Her face, broken
By nothing sharper than smiles, holds in its smiles
What I have forgotten.

She knows my father's dead,
And grieves for it, and smiles. She has digested
15 Mourning. Her smile shows it.

I, who need reminding
Every morning, shall never get over what
I do not remember.

Consistency matters.
20 I should like to keep faith with her lack of faith,
But forget her reasons.

Proud of this younger self,
I assert her achievements, her A levels,
Her job with a future.

25 Poor clever girl! I know,
For all my damaged brain, something she doesn't:
I am her future.

A bright girl she was.

POEM DICTIONARY
autocratic — powerful, assertive
Degas — an impressionist painter, who often painted ballet dancers

Casehistory: Alison (head injury)

Q1 The poet uses injury imagery in the poem. Copy the table and pick out images of injury from the poem and say what the effect of each one is.

We've put one here to start you off.

Image	Effect
Alison (head injury)	shows that Alison's injury is part of her identity

Q2 What is the effect of broken stanzas linked by enjambment, e.g. between lines 9 and 10?

Q3 Find a quotation from the poem which shows each of the following emotions:

a)   grief

b)   pride

c)   hope

d)   confusion

Q4 How does the narrator use pronouns like "she" and "I" to create distance between herself in the past and the present?

Q5 What does the line "A bright girl she was" show you about how Alison feels now?

Extension activity

- What do you think Fanthorpe is saying about mental health in this poem? Do you think the reader's attitude towards Alison as a narrator is affected by her brain damage?

You could link the themes in this poem with...

Injury: The Hunchback in the Park, p.10, On a Portrait of a Deaf Man, p.16; Identity: Checking Out Me History, p.18, Singh Song!, p.20, Les Grands Seigneurs, p.32, Medusa, p.26.

John Betjeman

John Betjeman (1906-1984) was born in London. He studied English at Oxford University, where his tutor was C. S. Lewis. As well as poetry, he wrote guidebooks and books on architecture, and was a prolific broadcaster. He was Poet Laureate from 1972 until his death in 1984.

On a Portrait of a Deaf Man

The kind old face, the egg-shaped head,
The tie, discreetly loud,
The loosely fitting shooting clothes,
A closely fitting shroud.

5   He liked old City dining-rooms,
Potatoes in their skin,
But now his mouth is wide to let
The London clay come in.

He took me on long silent walks
10 In country lanes when young.
He knew the names of ev'ry bird
But not the song it sung.

And when he could not hear me speak
He smiled and looked so wise
15 That now I do not like to think
Of maggots in his eyes.

He liked the rain-washed Cornish air
And smell of ploughed-up soil,
He liked a landscape big and bare
20 And painted it in oil.

But least of all he liked that place
Which hangs on Highgate Hill
Of soaked Carrara-covered earth
For Londoners to fill.

25 He would have liked to say good-bye,
Shake hands with many friends,
In Highgate now his finger-bones
Stick through his finger-ends.

You, God, who treat him thus and thus,
30 Say 'Save his soul and pray.'
You ask me to believe You and
I only see decay.

Graveyards look even creepier
when they're in greyscale

POEM DICTIONARY
shroud — funeral cloth
Carrara — type of marble used for headstones

Section One — Poems from the Literary Heritage

On a Portrait of a Deaf Man

Q1   Why do you think the poem is written in strict quatrains?

Q2   The narrator describes the dead man's tie as "discreetly loud".

    a)   What is this technique called? Choose the correct word below.

        oxymoron   alliteration   onomatopoeia

    b)   What does this tell us about what the dead man was like?

Q3   The poem includes lots of language related to the dead man's senses.
    Find an example from the poem which describes the following:

    a)   taste   b)   touch   c)   sight   d)   smell

Q4   a)   Why does the narrator use gruesome images to describe his father's dead body?

    b)   How does this contrast with the more conventional tributes to his personality?

Q5   What is the effect of the direct speech in line 30?

Q6   Explain the importance of the word "decay" at the end of the poem.

Extension activities

•   The poem could be read as an elegy to the narrator's dead father. Do you think it is
    a good tribute to the dead man? Give a reason for your answer.

•   Can you find any humour in the poem and, if so, what is its effect?

Other poems have similar themes...
<u>Death</u>: The River God, p.8, My Last Duchess, p.6, Medusa, p.26, Brendon Gallacher, p.28;
<u>Decay</u>: Ozymandias, p.4, The Clown Punk, p.22; <u>Grief</u>: Casehistory: Alison (head injury), p.14.

John Agard

Nanny
see-far woman
of mountain dream
fire-woman struggle
30   *hopeful stream*
to freedom river

Dem tell me bout Lord Nelson and Waterloo
but dem never tell me bout Shaka de great Zulu
Dem tell me bout Columbus and 1492
35   but what happen to de Caribs and de Arawaks too

Dem tell me bout Florence Nightingale and she lamp
and how Robin Hood used to camp
Dem tell me bout ole King Cole was a merry ole soul
but dem never tell me bout Mary Seacole

40   *From Jamaica*
she travel far
to the Crimean War
she volunteer to go
and even when de British said no
45   *she still brave the Russian snow*
a healing star
among the wounded
a yellow sunrise
to the dying

50   Dem tell me
Dem tell me wha dem want to tell me
But now I checking out me own history
I carving out me identity

POEM DICTIONARY
Toussaint L'Ouverture — ruler who led slaves to victory in the Haitian revolution
Nanny de Maroon — leader of the Maroons who led Jamaican resistance against the British
Lord Nelson — officer in the Royal Navy who died during the Battle of Trafalgar
Shaka — influential Zulu leader and warrior
Caribs and Arawaks — Caribbean people whose islands were invaded by Europeans
Mary Seacole — Jamaican nurse who helped to heal the sick in the Crimean War

John Agard

John Agard was born in Guyana in South America in 1949, to parents of mixed nationality. He came to Britain in 1977. He likes to perform his poems, and believes humour is an effective way of challenging people's opinions.

Checking Out Me History

Dem tell me
Dem tell me
Wha dem want to tell me

Bandage up me eye with me own history
5   Blind me to me own identity

Dem tell me bout 1066 and all dat
dem tell me bout Dick Whittington and he cat
But Toussaint L'Ouverture
no dem never tell me bout dat

10   *Toussaint*
        a slave
        with vision
        lick back
        Napoleon
15   *battalion*
        and first Black
        Republic born
        Toussaint de thorn
        to de French
20   *Toussaint de beacon*
        of de Haitian Revolution

Dem tell me bout de man who discover de balloon
and de cow who jump over de moon
Dem tell me bout de dish ran away with de spoon
25   but dem never tell me bout Nanny de maroon

THIS IS A FLAP.
FOLD THIS PAGE OUT.

Checking Out Me History

Q1   Why do you think the poet uses examples from British pantomime and nursery rhymes?

Q2   The poet talks about his feelings about his British education and Caribbean heritage.
Copy out the boxes below and put the following words into the correct boxes.

feelings about British education		feelings about Caribbean heritage
	pride resentment respect triumph anger disillusionment defiance joy	

Q3   Look at stanza four which begins, "Toussaint / a slave / with vision...".
Explain how the writer uses the following features in this stanza:

a)   rhyme   c)   sentence structure

b)   rhythm   d)   repetition

"I feel so good about the Caribbean right now."

Q4   Choose an image of vision or blindness from the poem and explain its effect.

Q5   Give an example of phonetic language from the poem.
Why do you think the poet has chosen to use it?

Q6   The tone changes at the end of the poem. Explain what you think the final line means.

Extension activity

•   Do some research and try to find out more about the people mentioned in the poem like Toussaint L'Ouverture and Nanny de Maroon. Does this help you to identify with the narrator?

Compare the themes in this poem with...
<u>Identity</u>: Singh Song!, p.20, Casehistory: Alison (head injury), p.14, The Clown Punk, p.22;
<u>Pride</u>: Ozymandias, p.4, The River God, p.8, Give, p.30, The Hunchback in the Park, p.10.

Daljit Nagra

my bride
　　she effing at my mum
　　in all di colours of Punjabi
25　　den stumble like a drunk
　　making fun at my daddy

my bride
　　tiny eyes ov a gun
　　and di tummy ov a teddy

30　my bride
　　she hav a red crew cut
　　and she wear a Tartan sari
　　a donkey jacket and some pumps
　　on di squeak ov di girls dat are pinching my sweeties —

35　Ven I return from di tickle ov my bride
　　di shoppers always point and cry:
　　Hey Singh, ver yoo bin?
　　Di milk is out ov date
　　and di bread is alvays stale,
40　*di tings yoo hav on offer yoo hav never got in stock*
　　in di worst Indian shop
　　on di whole Indian road —

　　Late in di midnight hour
　　ven yoo shoppers are wrap up quiet
45　ven di precinct is concrete-cool
　　vee cum down whispering stairs
　　and sit on my silver stool,
　　from behind di chocolate bars
　　vee stare past di half-price window signs
50　at di beaches ov di UK in di brightey moon —

　　from di stool each night she say,
　　　　How much do yoo charge for dat moon baby?

　　from di stool each night I say,
　　　　Is half di cost ov yoo baby,

55　from di stool each night she say,
　　　　How much does dat come to baby?

　　from di stool each night I say,
　　　　Is priceless baby —

POEM DICTIONARY
chapatti — an Indian flatbread
plantain — a kind of banana
sari — an Indian dress made up of a long length of material wrapped round the body
donkey jacket — a type of short coat, often worm by workmen

Daljit Nagra

Daljit Nagra was born in 1966 in West London to Punjabi parents. His poems reflect the experience of growing up as a British-born Indian. As well as writing poetry, he teaches English in a secondary school in London.

Singh Song!

I run just one ov my daddy's shops
from 9 o'clock to 9 o'clock
and he vunt me not to hav a break
but ven nobody in, I do di lock —

5   cos up di stairs is my newly bride
vee share in chapatti
vee share in di chutney
after vee hav made luv
like vee rowing through Putney —

10   Ven I return vid my pinnie untied
di shoppers always point and cry:
Hey Singh, ver yoo bin?
Yor lemons are limes
yor bananas are plantain,
15   *dis dirty little floor need a little bit of mop*
in di worst Indian shop
on di whole Indian road —

Above my head high heel tap di ground
as my vife on di web is playing wid di mouse
20   ven she netting two cat on her Sikh lover site
she book dem for di meat at di cheese ov her price —

THIS IS A FLAP.
FOLD THIS PAGE OUT.

Singh Song!

Q1   What is the narrator's attitude towards:

a)   the shoppers   b)   his father?

Q2   The poem contains many light-hearted images.

"Just imagine you're rowing
through Putney..."

a)   Pick out an image which you find humorous.

b)   What is the effect of using humour in the poem in general?

Q3   The narrator is married and talks about his "newly bride".
What evidence is there in the poem to show that he is a romantic man?

Q4   Why do you think the poet has chosen not to use Standard English punctuation?

Q5   The poem includes a chorus of irritated shoppers who complain to the shopkeeper.

a)   Do you think the customers are really angry at the shopkeeper?

b)   What is the effect of their phonetic speech in the poem?

Q6   What is the effect of the couple's conversation at the end of the poem?

Extension activity

• This poem is about British and Indian cultures. What do you think the poet is suggesting about the possibility of embracing the traditions of two different cultures?

Other poems have similar themes...

Identity: Casehistory: Alison (head injury), p.14, Checking Out Me History, p.18; Family: On a Portrait of a Deaf Man, p.16; Marriage: Les Grands Seigneurs, p.32, My Last Duchess, p.6.

Simon Armitage

Simon Armitage was born in 1963 in West Yorkshire. As well as poetry, he's also written four stage plays, and writes for TV, film and radio. He worked as a probation officer until 1994 and he now teaches at Manchester Metropolitan University.

The Clown Punk

Driving home through the shonky side of town,
three times out of ten you'll see the town clown,
like a basket of washing that got up
and walked, towing a dog on a rope. But

5   don't laugh: every pixel of that man's skin
is shot through with indelible ink;
as he steps out at the traffic lights,
think what he'll look like in thirty years' time –

the deflated face and shrunken scalp
10   still daubed with the sad tattoos of high punk.
You kids in the back seat who wince and scream
when he slathers his daft mush on the windscreen,

remember the clown punk with his dyed brain,
then picture windscreen wipers, and let it rain.

POEM DICTIONARY
shonky — derelict, run-down
indelible — permanent

The Clown Punk

Q1 Pick out an example of the following images:

    a)   a comical image of the punk

    b)   a sad image of the punk

    c)   a disturbing image of the punk

Q2 This poem is an unconventional sonnet.

    a)   What features of the poem tell you that this is a sonnet?

    b)   Why might the poet have chosen to write the poem using this form?

Q3 Does the impression given of the punk change from the beginning to the end of the poem? Back up your answer with evidence from the text.

Q4 Look at lines 5-6. What effect does the imagery create?

Q5 Why could the character of the clown punk be seen as ironic? Think about the normal meaning of the word "clown".

The girls were aiming for a modern-day rain dance.

Q6 What do you think the final phrase "let it rain" means?

Extension activities

- The narrator tells the children in the back of the car "don't laugh" and "remember the clown punk". Why do you think he's so concerned that the children think about the punk?

- Do you think the poem is based on a real experience?

Other poems touch on these themes...

Andrew Forster

Andrew Forster was born in South Yorkshire and lived in Scotland for 20 years. He used to work in social care but now works at the Wordsworth Trust and lives in Cumbria. His first poetry collection, 'Fear of Thunder', was published in 2007.

Horse Whisperer

They shouted for me
when their horses snorted, when restless
hooves traced circles in the earth
and shimmering muscles refused the plough.
5   My secret was a spongy tissue, pulled bloody
from the mouth of a just-born foal,
scented with rosemary, cinnamon,
a charm to draw the tender giants
to my hands.

10   They shouted for me
when their horses reared at burning straw
and eyes revolved in stately heads.
I would pull a frog's wishbone,
tainted by meat, from a pouch,
15   a new fear to fight the fear of fire,
so I could lead the horses,
like helpless children, to safety.

I swore I would protect
this legacy of whispers
20   but the tractor came over the fields
like a warning. I was the life-blood
no longer. From pulpits
I was scorned as demon and witch.
Pitchforks drove me from villages and farms.

25   My gifts were the tools of revenge.
A foul hex above a stable door
so a trusted stallion could be ridden
no more. Then I joined the stampede,
with others of my kind,
30   to countries far from our trade.

Still I miss them. Shire, Clydesdale, Suffolk.
The searing breath, glistening veins,
steady tread and the pride,
most of all the pride.

Sam was shocked when
the horse whispered back.

POEM DICTIONARY
hex — curse, evil spell
Shire, Clydesdale, Suffolk — breeds of horses

Section Two — Contemporary Poems

Horse Whisperer

Q1   Choose words to describe how the horse whisperer sees himself at the beginning of the poem.

proud	necessary	protector
useless	hated	powerful
hopeless	ignorant	talented

Q2   One of the images in the poem compares the horse whisperer to an animal.

    a)   Which image is this?

    b)   What is the effect of the image?

Q3   How does the horse whisperer's life change through the course of the poem?

Q4   Look at the line, "a new fear to fight the fear of fire".

    a)   What is this technique called? Choose the correct word below.

       euphemism   alliteration   onomatopoeia

    b)   What is the effect of the technique in this line?

Q5   What is the effect of using adjectives like "shimmering" and "glistening"?

Q6   How does the poet present ideas about the following themes:

    a)   revenge   b)   power   c)   pride

Extension activity

- Find out about what happened during the Industrial Revolution. What do you think the poet is saying about the effects of new technology on traditional trades?

You could compare this poem with...

Isolation: The Hunchback in the Park, p.10, Give, p.30, The Clown Punk, p.22; Religion: On a Portrait of a Deaf Man, p.16; Revenge: My Last Duchess, p.6, Medusa, p.26.

Section Two — Contemporary Poems

Carol Ann Duffy

<u>Carol Ann Duffy</u> was born in 1955 in Glasgow. She is Professor of Contemporary Poetry at Manchester Metropolitan University. She became Poet Laureate in 2009, the first woman to have held the position.

Medusa

A suspicion, a doubt, a jealousy
grew in my mind,
which turned the hairs on my head to filthy snakes,
as though my thoughts
5   hissed and spat on my scalp.

My bride's breath soured, stank
in the grey bags of my lungs.
I'm foul mouthed now, foul tongued,
yellow fanged.
10 There are bullet tears in my eyes.
Are you terrified?

Be terrified.
It's you I love,
perfect man, Greek God, my own;
15 but I know you'll go, betray me, stray
from home.
So better by far for me if you were stone.

I glanced at a buzzing bee,
a dull grey pebble fell
20 to the ground.
I glanced at a singing bird,
a handful of dusty gravel
spattered down.

I looked at a ginger cat,
25 a housebrick
shattered a bowl of milk.
I looked at a snuffling pig,
a boulder rolled
in a heap of shit.

30 I stared in the mirror.
Love gone bad
showed me a Gorgon.
I stared at a dragon.
Fire spewed
35 from the mouth of a mountain.

And here you come
with a shield for a heart
and a sword for a tongue
and your girls, your girls.
40 Wasn't I beautiful?
Wasn't I fragrant and young?

Look at me now.

Medusa

Q1   Look at this extract from the poem:

> "as though my thoughts
> hissed and spat on my scalp."

What is the effect of the "s" sounds in the highlighted words?

Q2   What impression do we get of the narrator's husband in the poem?

"If I can't see her,
she can't see me."

Q3   Why do you think the narrator uses childlike language such as "buzzing bee" and "snuffling pig"?

Q4   Copy the table, then write down quotes from the poem which show the following emotions:

Here's one to start you off.

Love	Hate	Vulnerability
"It's you I love"		

Q5   The final line is separated from the rest of the poem. What is the effect of this line?

Extension activities

- Do you think the narrator's marriage will end happily based on the evidence in the poem?

- Find out more about Medusa. Why do you think the poet chose this particular mythical monster for her character?

Several poems contain these themes...

Transformation: Les Grands Seigneurs, p.32, Casehistory: Alison (head injury), p.14, Ozymandias, p.4; Jealousy: My Last Duchess, p.6, The River God, p.8, The Ruined Maid, p.12.

Jackie Kay

Jackie Kay was born in 1961 in Edinburgh and brought up in Glasgow. As well as poetry, she's written novels, short stories and radio plays. She studied English at the University of Stirling and is a Professor of creative writing at Newcastle University. In 2006, she was awarded an MBE for services to literature.

Brendon Gallacher

He was seven and I was six, my Brendon Gallacher.
He was Irish and I was Scottish, my Brendon Gallacher.
His father was in prison; he was a cat burglar.
My father was a Communist Party full-time worker.
5　He had six brothers and I had one, my Brendon Gallacher.

He would hold my hand and take me by the river
where we'd talk all about his family being poor.
He'd get his mum out of Glasgow when he got older.
A wee holiday some place nice. Some place far.
10　I'd tell my mum about my Brendon Gallacher.

How his mum drank and his daddy was a cat burglar.
And she'd say, 'Why not have him round to dinner?'
No, no, I'd say, he's got big holes in his trousers.
I like meeting him by the burn in the open air.
15　Then one day after we'd been friends for two years,

one day when it was pouring and I was indoors,
my mum says to me, 'I was talking to Mrs Moir
who lives next door to your Brendon Gallacher.
Didn't you say his address was 24 Novar?
20　She says there are no Gallachers at 24 Novar.

There never have been any Gallachers next door.'
And he died then, my Brendon Gallacher,
flat out on my bedroom floor, his spiky hair,
his impish grin, his funny, flapping ear.
25　Oh Brendon. Oh my Brendon Gallacher.

"Boy, you're just a figment of my imagination."

<u>POEM DICTIONARY</u>
burn — stream

Section Two — Contemporary Poems

Brendon Gallacher

Q1 Find quotes from the poem which tell the reader about the narrator and Brendon. Copy out the table below then put the quotes in the correct column in the table.

Here's two to start you off.

Narrator	Brendon
"I was Scottish"	"He was Irish"

Q2 What is the effect of regional language such as "wee holiday"?

Q3 What is the effect of repetition in the poem?

Q4 How does the voice of the mother contrast with the imagined voice of the child?

Q5 What is the effect of the description, "his impish grin, his funny, flapping ear"?

Q6 What do you think Brendon Gallacher adds to the narrator's life that she doesn't have without him?

Q7 How does the tone of the poem change in line 22?

Extension activity

- Think about whether you or any of your friends had imaginary friends when you were growing up. What are some of the reasons that children create imaginary friends?

Other poems touch on these themes...
<u>Imagination</u>: Medusa, p.26; <u>Family</u>: On a Portrait of a Deaf Man, p.16, Singh Song!, p.20; <u>Grief</u>: Casehistory: Alison (head injury), p.14, My Last Duchess, p.6.

Simon Armitage

Simon Armitage was born in 1963 in West Yorkshire. As well as poetry, he's also written four stage plays, and writes for TV, film and radio. He worked as a probation officer until 1994 and he now teaches at Manchester Metropolitan University.

Give

Of all the public places, dear,
to make a scene, I've chosen here.

Of all the doorways in the world
to choose to sleep, I've chosen yours.
5   I'm on the street, under the stars.

For coppers I can dance or sing.
For silver — swallow swords, eat fire.
For gold — escape from locks and chains.

It's not as if I'm holding out
10   for frankincense or myrrh, just change.

You give me tea. That's big of you.
I'm on my knees. I beg of you.

Give

Q1   Explain how the narrator uses language associated with:

a)   homelessness   b)   unrequited love

Q2   a)   List all the things that the narrator says they will do for money.

b)   What does this suggest about the narrator's personality?

Q3   The narrator mentions "frankincense" and "myrrh" in line 10.
What is the significance of this?

Mmm, this sword
looks ever so tasty.

Q4   Why is the word "change" in line 10 ambiguous?

Q5   It could be argued that this poem is an unfinished sonnet.

a)   What features of this poem are like a sonnet? What features are different?

b)   Why is the form appropriate for the content of the poem?

Q6   How does the poet emphasise the narrator's desperation in the final two lines of the poem?

Extension activities

•   Pick out all the examples you can find of sarcasm in the poem. Why do you think the narrator is being sarcastic? Do you think they are trying to hide their true emotions?

•   Who do you think the "you" is that the narrator is talking to?

Compare the themes in this poem with...
Isolation: The Clown Punk, p.22, The Hunchback in the Park, p.10; Money: Singh Song!, p.20.

Dorothy Molloy

Dorothy Molloy (1942-2004) was born in County Mayo, Ireland. She studied languages at University College Dublin, then moved to Spain for some time, where she had considerable success as a painter. All three of her books of poems have been published posthumously.

Les Grands Seigneurs

Men were my buttresses, my castellated towers,
the bowers where I took my rest. The best and worst
of times were men: the peacocks and the cockatoos,
the nightingales, the strutting pink flamingos.

5   Men were my dolphins, my performing seals; my sailing-ships,
the ballast in my hold. They were the rocking-horses
prancing down the promenade, the bandstand
where the music played. My hurdy-gurdy monkey-men.

    I was their queen. I sat enthroned before them,
10 out of reach. We played at courtly love:
the troubadour, the damsel and the peach.

    But after I was wedded, bedded, I became
(yes, overnight) a toy, a plaything, little woman,
wife, a bit of fluff. My husband clicked
15 his fingers, called my bluff.

POEM DICTIONARY
Les Grands Seigneurs — French for 'The Great Lords'
buttresses — supporting structures for walls
castellated — having turrets like a castle
bowers — woman's bedroom in a medieval castle
ballast — weight used to keeps ships stable
hurdy-gurdy — a type of organ (traditionally the organ-grinder had a monkey with him)
troubadour — travelling medieval folk singer

Go, horsey, go.

Les Grands Seigneurs

Q1 Copy the table then find images which present the men as protective, entertaining and silly.

Here's one to start you off.

Protective	Entertaining	Silly
"buttresses"		

Q2 How does the narrator's opinion of herself change throughout the poem?

Q3 The poet uses imagery from the courtly love tradition.

In the courtly love tradition, men did brave deeds to win their lover's affection.

a) Pick out three courtly love images from the poem.

b) Why has the poet chosen to use this type of imagery?

"My, what big tail feathers you have..."

Q4 Why do you think the narrator describes the men using metaphors like "peacocks" and "dolphins" instead of personal details?

Q5 Why do you think the poet has written "(yes, overnight)" in brackets in line 13?

Q6 What does the narrator mean when she says that her husband "clicked / his fingers, called my bluff"?

Extension activities

- Write out the first three stanzas of the poem using modern imagery instead of courtly love imagery. What effect does this have on the poem?

- Why do you think the title of the poem is written in French?

Other poems feature these themes...

Character

Q1   List as many poems from the cluster as you can which you think feature the following characters:

   a)   imaginary characters

   b)   characters without a voice

   c)   fantasy characters

Q2   Choose a poem from the cluster that describes a powerful character.

   a)   How does the poet present the power of the character?

   b)   Can you think of a character with a similar kind of power from another poem?

   c)   What is the poet's message about the character's power?

Q3   Choose a different poem with a character in it. Write down three words to describe the character and explain why you have chosen those words. Use the box below for some ideas.

proud	arrogant	vulnerable
deluded	vicious	destructive
terrifying	furious	romantic

Q4   Pick two characters from the following list which you think have something in common. Explain why you have linked them together.

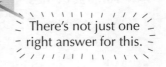
There's not just one right answer for this.

   •   the narrator in 'Brendon Gallacher'

   •   Alison in 'Casehistory: Alison (head injury)'

   •   the hunchback in 'The Hunchback in the Park'

   •   the king in 'Ozymandias'

Voice

Q1   Choose a poem that has a first person narrator. Explain the effect of this kind of narrative voice in the poem you have chosen.

Q2   Copy and complete the table to show which poems use these kinds of voices.

Dramatic monologue	Dramatic dialogue	Internal monologue	Many voices

In a dramatic monologue, the person listening doesn't speak, but in a dramatic dialogue, they do.

This is where you hear a character's inner thoughts.

Q3   Choose a poem from the cluster. Write down three words to describe the tone of voice and explain why that is appropriate to the poem. Look in the box below for some ideas.

> sad   nostalgic   arrogant
>
> proud   confident   triumphant
>
> angry   grieving   desperate

Q4   Choose two poems that contain a childlike voice.

     a)   Suggest why each poet uses this voice.

     b)   Compare how this language has an effect on the reader.

Can you say "iambic pentameter"...?

Exam-Style Questions

Remember to make a proper <u>plan</u> before you start writing out your answer.

0 5   Compare how characters are presented in *My Last Duchess* and **one** other poem from 'Characters and Voices'.

                                                        (36 marks)

0 6   Compare how voice is shown in *Checking Out Me History* and **one** other poem from 'Characters and Voices'.

                                                        (36 marks)

Power

Q1 Copy the table and list the poems in the cluster which present power as positive and the ones which present it as negative.

Power as **positive**	Power as **negative**

Q2 From any poem in the cluster, find an example of the following language devices that are used to create a sense of power:

Marion was impressed by Ed's powerful arms.

a)   imperatives (commands)

b)   possessive language

c)   metaphors

Q3 Compare how the Duke in 'My Last Duchess' and the narrator in 'The River God' show their power over women.

Q4 Some characters have a lack of power. Pick out a poem which features a powerless character and describe how they deal with their lack of power.

Q5 Characters can seem powerful when they are actually weak and vulnerable.

a)   Pick a poem from the cluster which features a character like this.

b)   Explain how the poet presents the character as both powerful and weak.

c)   What is the effect of this on the reader?

Death

Q1   "All the poems in this cluster present death as a negative thing." Do you agree?

Q2   Choose a poem from 'Characters and Voices' which could be described as an elegy. Is the poem a conventional or unconventional elegy? Give reasons for your answer.

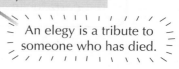

An elegy is a tribute to someone who has died.

Q3   Name a poem from the cluster which portrays each of these emotions about death:

    a) delusion   b) horror   c) pride   d) sadness

Q4   Choose a poem about the death of a way of life or civilisation. How is this 'death' presented?

Q5   Create a table like the one below to show how two of the poems use language to present feelings and attitudes about death.

Poem	Language to present death	Feelings/attitudes about death

Exam-Style Questions

| 0 | 6 | Compare how power is presented in _Ozymandias_ and **one** other poem from 'Characters and Voices'. | _(36 marks)_ |

| 0 | 7 | Compare how poets use language to express ideas about death in _On a Portrait of a Deaf Man_ and **one** other poem from 'Characters and Voices'. | _(36 marks)_ |

Section Three — Themes

Damage

Q1   Which of the characters are physically damaged? Which are emotionally damaged?

Medusa	the Clown Punk	the Duchess
the Hunchback	the River God	the horse whisperer
the narrator in 'Give'	Alison	Melia

Q2   Choose one of the characters from Q1 that is physically damaged.

   a)   How does the physical damage affect the character's personality?

   b)   How does the damage affect the character's relationships with others?

Q3   Choose two of the characters from Q1 that are mentally damaged.

   a)   Write down all the words from this list which apply to both characters.

deluded	vulnerable	in pain
angry	unfeeling	loving
bitter	confused	grieving
unstable	childlike	frustrated

   b)   Find quotes from both poems to support each of the words.

   c)   Which character do you think is more damaged and why?

Q4   "None of the poems in this cluster offer any hope for the future." Do you agree?
Give evidence from the poems to support your answer.

Section Three — Themes

Men and Women

Q1   Relationships between men and women can be shown to be happy or unhappy. Copy this table, then list poems from the cluster in the right column.

Happy relationships	Unhappy relationships	Mixed feelings

They hadn't looked at each other for 5 years and couldn't be happier.

Q2   Choose a poem in which a woman's feelings towards men have changed.

    a)   How did she feel about men in the past?

    b)   What does she think about men now?

Q3   Do you think men or women are presented as more possessive in relationships? Back up your answer with evidence from the poems.

Q4   Choose two poems which explore relationships between men and women. Pick one from the 'Contemporary Poems' section and one from the 'Literary Heritage' section of the anthology.

    a)   What is the attitude to relationships in each poem?

    b)   Do you think the time each poem was written has influenced the poet's attitude to relationships between men and women?

Exam-Style Questions

0 5   Compare how *Casehistory: Alison (head injury)* and **one** other poem from 'Characters and Voices' present the effects of physical or emotional damage.   *(36 marks)*

0 6   Compare how poets present relationships between men and women in *Les Grands Seigneurs* and **one** other poem from 'Characters and Voices'.   *(36 marks)*

Section Three — Themes

Pride

Q1   Write down these characters in order from most proud to least proud in your opinion.

- the River God in *The River God*
- the king in *Ozymandias*
- the punk in *The Clown Punk*
- the hunchback in *The Hunchback in the Park*
- the narrator in *Checking Out Me History*
- the horse whisperer in *Horse Whisperer*

Q2   "All the poems in the anthology portray pride in a negative way."   Do you agree?

Q3   Choose two poems which feature arrogant characters.

What kind of language does the poet use to emphasise the characters' arrogance?

Q4   The narrator in *Give* seems proud at first, but his feelings change later in the poem. How do we know that he isn't actually proud of his situation?

Q5   Some of the poets present characters in their poems who are proud of their culture. Compare the language used by two characters who are proud of their heritage.

Q6   Choose a poem from the cluster that features a character who is mistakenly proud.

a)   Write down a quote from the poem which shows that their pride isn't justified.

b)   What is the poet's message about this kind of pride?

Identity

Q1 Draw a spider diagram showing all the things you can think of that make up a person's identity.

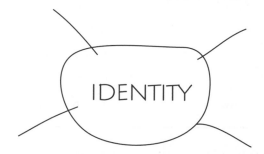

IDENTITY

Don't worry, spider diagrams don't bite.

Q2 Some characters change their identities through the course of the poem. Copy the table then fill it in to show how each character has changed.

Character	Identity in the past	Identity in the present
narrator in *Les Grands Seigneurs*		
narrator in *Checking Out Me History*		
Melia in *The Ruined Maid*		
narrator in *Medusa*		

Q3 What do the poems *Checking Out Me History* and *Les Grands Seigneurs* suggest about how we create our own identity?

Q4 Look at two poems which feature characters who are uncertain about their identity. How does each poet use form to present the character's search for identity?

Exam-Style Questions

| 0 | 5 | Compare how pride is presented in *The River God* and **one** other poem from 'Characters and Voices'. | *(36 marks)* |

| 0 | 6 | Compare how *Singh Song!* and **one** other poem from 'Characters and Voices' use language and dialect to explore a character's identity. | *(36 marks)* |

42

Negative Emotions

Q1   a)   Link these quotes expressing negative emotions with the poem they come from.

"You give me tea. That's big of you."	*Ozymandias*
"My gifts were the tools of revenge."	*Medusa*
"sneer of cold command"	*Horse Whisperer*
"I know you'll go, betray me"	*Give*
"If she wishes to go I will not forgive her."	*The River God*

   b)   Identify which negative emotion is expressed in each quote.

Q2   Choose a poem which contains anger. How is that anger portrayed?

Q3   Choose two poems which portray characters with negative emotions.

Compare the ways the poets use language to present these negative emotions.

Q4   How can negative emotions create problems in a relationship?
Back up your answer by referring to three poems.

Q5   Some characters are justified in their negative emotions because of their circumstances.
Choose a character from the cluster who you think shows the following and give a reason:

   a)   A character who has a good reason for their negative feelings.

   b)   A character who does not have a good reason for their negative feelings.

   c)   A character who tries to hide their negative feelings.

   d)   A character who is confused about their negative feelings.

Decay

Q1   The poets in this cluster present the theme of decay in lots of different ways.

Use a thesaurus to look up words connected to decay,
then try to say which of the poems they apply to.

Q2   Copy and complete the table, giving an example of how the poet presents
the physical decay of the body and an explanation of the quote.

Here's an example
to help you out.

Poem	Quote	Explanation
On a Portrait of a Deaf Man	"maggots in his eyes"	his father's decaying body disgusts him, but he cannot stop thinking about it
Medusa		
The Clown Punk		
Casehistory: Alison (head injury)		

Q3   Choose a poem which uses form to emphasise the
theme of decay and explain how the poet does this.

Q4   Poets don't just talk about physical decay. What other kinds of decay can
you find in this cluster? Give an example from a poem for each one.

Q5   Choose a poem which shows the negative effects of ageing.
How does the character feel about ageing in the poem?

Albert couldn't wait to
get his free bus pass.

Exam-Style Questions

0 6   Compare how negative emotions are presented in *Medusa* and
one other poem from 'Characters and Voices'.   *(36 marks)*

0 7   Compare how the poet presents decay in *On a Portrait of a Deaf Man*
and **one** other poem from 'Characters and Voices'.   *(36 marks)*

Mark Scheme

This section is a bit <u>different</u> — it's your chance to get inside the <u>examiner's mind</u>.

1) The mark scheme below is <u>very similar</u> to the one that the <u>examiners will use</u> to mark your actual exam answers.

2) The point of this section is to understand exactly what the examiners are <u>looking for</u> and <u>what you'll need to do</u> on the day to get high marks.

3) You have to <u>read</u> the <u>sample extracts</u> of exam answers. Then you'll either <u>mark</u> the answer and say how it can be <u>improved</u>, or add some <u>extra points</u> to make the answer better. The <u>mark scheme</u> will help you do this.

4) Before you start grading the sample answers, make sure you've read the mark scheme really <u>thoroughly</u> and that you <u>understand everything</u>.

Grade	What you've written
A*	• Explores several interpretations or meanings in detail • Provides carefully chosen and well-integrated quotes to back up ideas • Compares the poems thoughtfully and in detail, using plenty of evidence • Looks closely at <u>how</u> language, form and structure affect the reader with well-chosen examples • Gives detailed and imaginative ideas about themes, attitudes and feelings • Considers the evidence to come up with conclusions about the poem
A	• Gives several interpretations or meanings • Provides well-chosen quotes to support ideas • Compares the poems in detail and provides plenty of evidence • Describes <u>how</u> language, form and structure affect the reader, using examples • Looks at themes, attitudes and feelings in detail, again using plenty of evidence
B	• Thoughtful interpretation of the poems • Supports interpretations with quotes from the text • Provides some well-chosen evidence to support comparisons between the poems • Gives several examples of <u>how</u> language, form and structure affect the reader • Provides some evidence to support ideas about themes, attitudes and feelings
C	• Comments on several aspects of the poem, e.g. mood, language, feelings, and uses quotes to back the comments up • Makes several comparisons between the poems • Explains <u>how</u> language, form and structure affect the reader • Makes valid comments about themes, attitudes or feelings in the poems

You'll also be marked on your <u>spelling</u>, <u>punctuation</u> and <u>grammar</u> and on how you <u>present</u> your work. To get the <u>best marks</u>, your essay should be <u>clearly organised</u> into <u>well-structured</u> paragraphs. It should also be <u>easy</u> to follow and <u>understand</u>.

Adding Quotes and Developing Points

The sample answers on this page have just one thing missing. Your task is to improve each point by adding a quote from the poem which backs it up. Good luck...

| 0 | 1 | Compare how ideas about identity are presented in *Checking Out Me History* and one other poem from 'Characters and Voices'. *(36 marks)* |

Answer Extract 1

In this sample answer, some sentences have letters like this: **(A)**.
Replace each letter with a suitable quote to help the student get a better grade.

> In both 'Checking Out Me History' and 'Singh Song!', the poets show the reader how important identity is to people. Agard describes the way he has only been taught the British version of history. He seems to feel that this is a deliberate action and he uses images such as **(A)** to show this. In 'Singh Song!', Nagra uses the stereotypical idea of Indian people running shops. He describes his father as hard working, but he is clearly not like his father because he admits, **(B)**.
> Both poems suggest that identity is individual and cannot be forced on them. In 'Singh Song!', the Indian man does not seem to share his father's work ethic. At the end of 'Checking Out Me History', Agard uses much more positive language, such as **(C)**, to emphasise that knowing his history will help him find his own identity.

Answer Extract 2

In this sample answer, some sentences have letters like this: **(A)**.
Replace each letter with a suitable quote to help the student get a better grade.

> Both 'Checking Out Me History' and 'Singh Song!' show that identity is made up of different elements. Agard describes examples of the history he was taught when he was growing up, such as **(A)**, but he feels that this is not his own history. This makes it clear that he feels that there are two elements to his character: the British side and the Caribbean side.
> There is a similar idea in 'Singh Song!' because the couple do things which show they are influenced by their Indian culture, like **(B)**. However, they also behave in ways which are clearly British, not Indian, for example **(C)**. This shows that their identity is made up of both Indian and British parts.

Adding Quotes and Developing Points

Two more tasks on this page — develop the points and finish the plan.

> **0 1** Compare how ideas about identity are presented in *Checking Out Me History* and one other poem from 'Characters and Voices'. *(36 marks)*

Answer Extract 3

In this sample answer, some sentences have letters like this: **(A)**. These points need to be developed further. Write an extra sentence or two to develop each point.

> Agard talks about the differences between what "dem tell me" and the things that they never mention. He is taught all about key events from British history and childish stories such as "de cow who jump over de moon", but he does not know about important figures from black history like Toussaint L'Ouverture. **(A)**
>
> Nagra takes a different view about his roots. He describes how he is in charge of "one ov my daddy's shops", which is a stereotypical view of what British Indian people do for a living. Unlike Agard, he does not seem to be very proud of this — he reports that people tell him that it is "di worst Indian shop / on di whole Indian road". **(B)** He seems more proud of the modern parts of his life. His wife is not a traditional Indian woman but the narrator says she is "priceless".
>
> Both poems are written as though they are being spoken. In 'Checking Out Me History', the stanzas about British history are written in regular metre and form, but the stanzas about the history that he is interested in are irregular. In 'Singh Song!', the poem is written like a song with verses and a chorus. It has also got lots of repetition, like "from di stool each night I say" in the last stanza. **(C)**

> **0 2** Compare the ways in which characters are presented in *Ozymandias* and one other poem in 'Characters and Voices'. *(36 marks)*

Sample Plan

The table below is a plan for an answer to the question above.

Find a quotation from the poem to back up each of the language points in the table.
Make brief notes on your personal response to each poem to complete the plan.

	Ozymandias	My Last Duchess
Themes and ideas	Power of humans / time. Celebration of life?	Controlling someone else. Portrait — celebration?
Language	Of arrogance / power ... **(A)** Of irony ... **(B)**	Of power ... **(C)** Of death / murder ... **(D)**
Form and Structure	Sonnet, but not about love. Unusual rhyme scheme — things are out of balance	Dramatic monologue — only from the Duke's point of view. Sudden changes of topic
Personal Response	**(E)**	**(F)**

Section Four — Analysing Answers

Marking Answer Extracts

This page is all about marking sample exam answers. If you're reading this without reading the mark scheme on p.44 first — do not collect £200 and certainly DO NOT pass GO.

---

0 2 Compare the ways in which characters are presented in *Ozymandias* and one other poem in 'Characters and Voices'. *(36 marks)*

Answer Extract 4

1) Use the mark scheme to <u>mark</u> this extract to the question above.

2) <u>Explain</u> how you decided on the grade and say how the answer could be <u>improved</u>.

> In both 'Ozymandias' and 'My Last Duchess', the characters want to show their power. Ozymandias had the statue of himself built to show how powerful he was. In the second poem, there seems to have been a power struggle. The Duke has power because he was able to give the Duchess "My gift of a nine-hundred-years-old name", but he was not able to control her in the way that he wanted to when she was alive. It was only when he "gave commands" that he was able to make her behave how he wanted her to, and he now has total control over her painting. Both poems seem at first to be celebrating lives, but when you read them more deeply, it seems that the poets might be telling us that, in reality, individuals are fairly insignificant.

This first extract has been <u>marked for you</u> to show you what to do.

Response: This answer gets a grade **B** because it talks about the themes of the poems and how the language, structure and form affect the reader, and provides examples of these things. It could be improved by analysing language in more detail and providing less obvious interpretations.

---

0 3 Compare how feelings about people are presented in *Horse Whisperer* and one other poem from 'Characters and Voices'. *(36 marks)*

Answer Extract 5

1) Use the mark scheme on p.44 to <u>mark</u> this extract.

2) <u>Explain</u> how you decided on the grade and say how the answer could be <u>improved</u>.

> 'Horse Whisperer' is a poem which harks back to the past and describes a particular person's way of life and his beliefs. 'On a Portrait of a Deaf Man' also looks back on someone's life.
> Forster describes the skills that the horse whisperer had — he could "lead the horses" thanks to his "secret" skills. Similarly, Betjeman suggests that his father was a knowledgeable man. He "knew the names of ev'ry bird / But not the song it sung". The fact that both poems are written about specific people encourages the reader to think that the poets must have been proud of them to want to immortalise them in poetry.

Marking Answer Extracts

Here's the same exam question again and another extract from a sample answer to it.

| 0 | 3 | Compare how feelings about people are presented in *Horse Whisperer* and one other poem from 'Characters and Voices'. *(36 marks)* |

Answer Extract 6

1) Use the mark scheme on p.44 to <u>mark</u> this extract.
2) <u>Explain</u> how you decided on the grade and how you think it could be <u>improved</u>.

The opening line of 'Horse Whisperer' suggests that other people respected his skill because, in times of need, "They shouted for me". Forster makes it clear, through his choice of language, that the horse whisperer has a genuine skill as he can "lead the horses, / like helpless children" and "draw the tender giants / to my hands". This suggests to the reader that the poet has a sense of genuine admiration for this person.

The same is also true of 'On a Portrait of a Deaf Man', where the man is immediately described as having a "kind old face". This sets the scene for a positive poem which will show the sense of pride that the poet feels in his father. This becomes even more clear when he describes how "He knew the names of ev'ry bird / But not the song it sung."

As well as celebrating these people, both poets show how things have changed. In 'On a Portrait of a Deaf Man', the man with the "egg-shaped head" has died and "now his mouth is wide to let / The London clay come in." For Betjeman, this new situation is too much for him to think about and he tells the reader that "I do not like to think" of the bad things that have happened to him.

Keep looking back at the mark scheme so you know exactly what you should be looking for — don't just think "Oh, it's not bad, I'll give it a C".

Marking Answer Extracts

Same question, different sample answer. Hopefully you're getting into the examiner's mind-set by now...

| 0 | 3 | Compare how feelings about people are presented in *Horse Whisperer* and one other poem from 'Characters and Voices'.   *(36 marks)* |

Answer Extract 7

1) Use the mark scheme on p.44 to <u>mark</u> this extract.

2) <u>Explain</u> how you decided on the grade and say how the answer could be <u>improved</u>.

Don't forget to keep looking back at the mark scheme!

Both 'Horse Whisperer' and 'On a Portrait of a Deaf Man' are poems about people and how attitudes to them can change over time. In 'Horse Whisperer', it seems that it is the man's skill with animals which is being celebrated, whilst in 'On a Portrait of a Deaf Man', the deaf man is important not only for being the poet's father, but also for his wisdom.

Both poems open with a strong indication of the poet's admiration. The old man is described by Betjeman as having a "kind old face", which suggests tenderness and affection, whilst Forster describes how "They shouted for me", which implies that people called on his services when they were most in need. This immediately suggests to the reader that these people are both special, although in different ways.

Both poets give the reader a very clear sense of the person they are describing. We know that the horse whisperer used charms and "a frog's wishbone" to calm the horses so that he was able to help them to "fight the fear". He sounds like a mysterious but trustworthy character who treated the horses like "helpless children". The same is also true of the old man who "liked old City dining-rooms" and "smiled and looked so wise" even when he couldn't hear his son speaking. In both cases, the vivid descriptions help the reader to engage with the character and the poet's feelings about them.

It is shocking to us, therefore, that both poems show a change in the ways the characters are described. The man with the "egg-shaped head" dies and now has "maggots in his eyes" whilst he lies in "that place / Which hangs on Highgate Hill". This horrific image contrasts sharply with the affectionate descriptions earlier in the poem. The same is true of the horse whisperer, who suddenly changes from being "the life-blood" to being "scorned as demon and witch", and we can understand why he might then join "the stampede" to escape from the accusations.

Nobody's coming near my wishbone...

Marking a Complete Answer

New page, new question and answer. Only this time it's the whole answer, not just an extract...

| 0 | 4 | Compare how characters are presented in *Les Grands Seigneurs* and one other poem in 'Characters and Voices'. *(36 marks)* |

Answer 8

Make sure you've read the advice and mark scheme on page 44.

Read the whole answer. Use the mark scheme to mark the answer.
Explain how you decided on the grade and say how the answer could be improved.

> Both 'Les Grands Seigneurs' and 'Medusa' explore ideas about characters and their relationships from the points of view of women. In the first poem, the narrator explores her past relationships and the ways in which she has treated men, where she seems to have always been the one in control. The second poem, on the other hand, is about the narrator's current relationship, in which she seems to have no control whatsoever.
>
> In 'Les Grands Seigneurs', the narrator describes the men in her past life as "my buttresses, my castellated towers", which suggests that she saw them as the supports in her life. These images link to the ideas of courtly love in which men were considered to be strong and powerful and women relied upon them. She also describes them as being "my performing seals", which implies that their function was to entertain her whilst she was "out of reach". The idea of courtly love gives the woman the power because she is untouchable and remote, with men at her beck and call.
>
> In contrast, the narrator in 'Medusa' seems to have no power at all. She seems afraid and angry because the power in her relationship belongs to her husband, thanks to the "suspicion" that she feels over his fidelity. Even when she describes her anger "as though my thoughts / hissed and spat on my scalp", she seems to be afraid. Personified as the Gorgon Medusa, she uses verbs in the past tense such as "glanced" and "looked" to show that her anger has caused her to take action, turning a "singing bird" into "a handful of dusty gravel" with the force of her anger and hate. Although this language suggests that she has power, it is not the right kind of power to make her husband love her.
>
> 'Les Grands Seigneurs' means "the great lords" and I think this is an interesting title for the poem. Molloy seems to be suggesting that the men in her past were great, but this comes across as an ironic statement. When she describes men as her "rocking-horses... My hurdy-gurdy monkey-men" she is mocking the way in which they have behaved, and that makes the title ironic. Duffy's description of the husband as "perfect man, Greek God, my own" is ironic because she knows, and so does the reader, that he must be far from perfect if he is cheating on her with his "girls".

Marking a Complete Answer

This is the second half of the answer on p.50.

In both poems, the structure helps the reader to understand the changing emotions of the characters. Molloy uses free verse which sounds almost conversational, helping the reader to relate to her ideas. It feels as if she is confiding a secret to her reader. The first three stanzas all concentrate on her past relationships, where she was the person who had all of the power. However, she tells us that "We played at courtly love", which suggests that she always knew that it was a game and that it would not last. In the final stanza, she reveals that her life in the present is very different from her relationships in the past. She tells us that she was "wedded, bedded" and then describes how her life has been different ever since. She is no longer in control and is now "a toy, a plaything, little woman". The idea of a "little woman" is fairly negative and makes her seem as though she has no power at all any more, and that she is just a belonging. The fact that she ends the poem with the phrase "called my bluff" suggests that she was shocked and surprised by what happened to her.

In 'Medusa', it is at the end of the poem that the narrator reveals the person behind the "filthy snakes". She has seemed powerful and angry throughout the poem, but she changes from making angry and violent statements to asking "Wasn't I beautiful? / Wasn't I fragrant and young?" This changes the mood of the poem and the reader gets a sense that she is vulnerable and afraid of what has happened to her. In the final line, which is isolated from the rest, she says, "Look at me now", which could be her begging him to look at what he has done to her. The fact that it is separate suggests that she feels isolated and distanced from her husband.

Both poems have a strong impact on the reader, partly because they are both about feelings that most people can understand. The fact that Molloy's heroine is reduced from a powerful "queen" to nothing but "a bit of fluff" creates a negative image of how a marriage can change someone so completely. It also makes us wonder whether it is something that is inevitable. This is similar to Medusa because we feel sorry for the fact that her "bride's breath soured, stank" as a result of her jealous suspicions. Both poems explore strong and real feelings and make readers think about their own lives.

Acknowledgements

The Publisher would like to thank:

John Agard: 'Checking Out Me History' — copyright © 1996 by John Agard reproduced by kind permission of John Agard c/o Caroline Sheldon Literary Agency Limited

Simon Armitage: 'The Clown Punk' — From *Tyrannosaurus Rex Versus the Corduroy Kid* (Faber and Faber, 2007)

Simon Armitage: 'Give' — From *The Dead Sea Poems* Faber and Faber (5 Nov 2001)

John Betjeman: 'On a Portrait of a Deaf Man' — From *Collected Poems*, by John Betjeman © 1955, 1958, 1962, 1964, 1968, 1970, 1979, 1981, 1982, 2001. Reproduced by permission of John Murray (Publishers)

Carol Ann Duffy: 'Medusa' — Reproduced with the permission of Picador, an imprint of Pan Macmillan, London. Copyright © Carol Ann Duffy 2000

U A Fanthorpe: 'Casehistory: Alison (head injury)' — U A Fanthorpe, from *Collected Poems* 1978-2003, Peterloo Poets, 2005

Andrew Forster: 'Horse Whisperer' — From *Fear of Thunder* (Flambard Press)

Jackie Kay: 'Brendon Gallacher' — Jackie Kay, *Darling: New & Selected Poems* (Bloodaxe Books, 2007)

Dorothy Molloy: 'Les Grands Seigneurs' — From *Hare Soup*, Faber and Faber (19 Feb 2004)

Daljit Nagra: 'Singh Song!' — From *Look We Have Coming to Dover!*, Faber and Faber; 1st ed. (1 Feb 2007)

Stevie Smith: 'The River God' — Estate of James MacGibbon

Dylan Thomas: 'The Hunchback in the Park' — From *Collected Poems* 1934-1952 (Dent, 1952) reproduced by permission of David Higham